AN ACORN HOUSE BOOK
STORY BOOKS OF THE OPERA SERIES

THE STORY OF

VERDI'S FAMOUS OPERA

AIDA

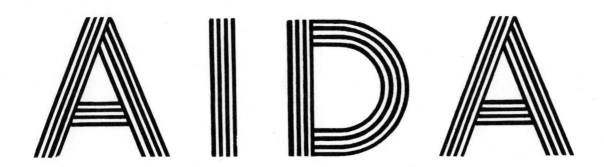

TOLD BY DORTHA M. TAYLOR

MUSICAL THEMES ARRANGED BY JOHN GOLDMARK

ILLUSTRATED BY WILLIAM O'DONOVAN

CONTENTS

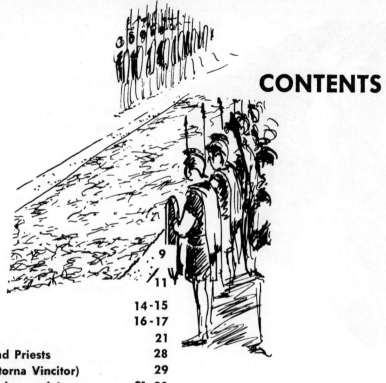

THE CAST

AIDA (Ah-ee'-da) *Soprano*
RADAMES (Rahd'ah-maze) *Tenor*
AMNERIS (Am-nay'-riss) *Contralto*
AMONASRO (Ah-mo-nazz'-row) *Baritone*
RAMPHIS (Rahm'-fiss) *Bass*

ACT I: *Scene 1*

The high priest of the goddess Isis stared into space.

"It is truly grave," he said in his chant-like voice. "I have brought you here, Radames, to tell you privately what soon everyone will know. The tribes of the Ethiopians are attacking the city of Thebes in the valley of the Nile."

He made a sweeping gesture. "Don't interrupt me, Radames. It is the latest news and it has been confirmed. Our army will march against them, of course, for Memphis and Egypt are not helpless. But Memphis, our beloved city, and Egypt, our beloved land, need a brave and wise and young general to lead that army."

The high priest turned toward Radames, standing so tall beside him, looking so young in his uniform. Slowly the high priest closed his eyes then opened them half-way like a cat. He looked long at Radames. Then he spoke again.

"At this very moment in the Temple sacred to Isis the pale wands of incense are pointing the signs of choice, the mysterious signs of choice. This morning before the sun was shining on the Nile, there arose murmuring from behind the golden curtain. It meant that Isis was about to choose the warrior who is to lead our country into battle. Isis," he continued in his chant-like voice, "Isis does not forget her people. Isis is choosing."

He inclined his head. Radames wet his lips, but the high priest Ramphis held up both hands for silence. Then turning sharply away, he glided between the pillars of the long colonnade and passed into the sunshine among the palm trees in the direction of the pyramids and the Temple of Isis.

The young warrior Radames was left alone in the great hall of the King of Memphis.

"Then it's true. The
rumors were right for once.
And even in the streets
they were saying a new
leader would be chosen to
lead the army. But why,
then, did he decide to tell
me? Does he mean *me?*
This Ramphis talks of
mystery and nothing but
mystery. Yet he never said
ten words to me before—
and now he brings me here
and gives me this long speech."

Radames sighed. "Really,
I must be asleep and dreaming.
Ever since Aida came to Memphis

I believe I've been dreaming. Lovely Aida!"

He thumped the column beside him. The cool stone was solid. He ran a finger in the chiseled lines of a hieroglyph.

"What will she say when she hears of the invasion? Will she still love me if I'm called to kill her countrymen? Will she wish herself dead like she did when she was first captured?" Now Radames too stared into space, only his eyes soon began to smile and his lips to form a kiss.

"To wherever you are, Aida," he whispered. "Somewhere in this palace of a thousand rooms this kiss will find you and send you to walk again in the olive gardens. We can talk together there and no one will see us."

Radames entire face was smiling now as he sang to himself the song of his beautiful Aida:

CELESTE AIDA   With feeling

CELESTE AIDA (concluded)

ACT 1

Scene 1

Radames stopped his wandering hand. He stood motionless, the tender glow of love on his face. "You are perfect, Aida. Your hands—your face— beautiful. The princess of perfection. And I will make you a princess, too, if we are victorious. I'll return you to your own country and set you on the throne there. They will find you as splendid as the sun. And I can do it, too. I, captain, leader of the victorious Egyptians! Then . . ." and Radames' face broke into a shower of joy, "then—"

"How absorbed you are!"

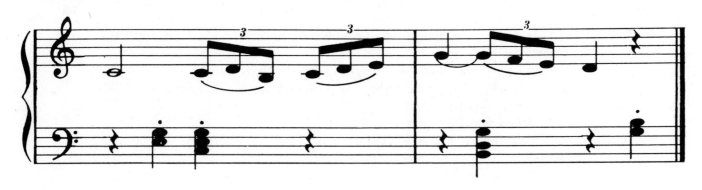

Radames whirled about. The daughter of the King of Memphis stood beside him. She waved a palm fan under his nose as though it were smelling salts.

"You men, how absorbed you are! And it is something very pleasant, too, for your face to be sparkling so."

"Oh, I beg your pardon," Radames was so embarrassed he interrupted the princess as he bowed.

"And yet," she continued, playfully tapping him on the nose with her fan, "sparkling isn't quite right. No, I should say it was something much more interesting to women."

Radames was turning red.

"Come now, what is it you were thinking of?" persisted the princess Amneris.

"Your highness, I was thinking—I should say hoping—," and Radames took a deep breath, "that I might be chosen general to lead the armies against the invaders. It was this thought you just saw on my face."

He began to bow again.

"So," the princess Amneris said slowly. "Yet I have seen you here often looking much the same before any armies or invaders were about."

Four trumpets sounded in the distance.

"Surely," she continued, "if you look this way upon war, how much fonder you must look upon love. How lucky is the woman who excites love from you."

The princess Amneris began to admire the two royal rings on each of her hands.

"What strong tapering fingers you have," she said to Radames. "Something like my own. Do you suppose one of my rings would fit on your little finger?" She began to tug at a sapphire.

"Some one's coming," murmured Radames in a tight voice, and only too glad for the interruption, he stepped back to a more respectful distance.

But the princess Amneris again moved close. "What a bother! Always someone coming or someone going. Shall we ignore them—they'll go away if we do?" She was looking into Radames' strained face for an answer. What she saw there made her turn sharply.

"Aida, so it's you!" she exclaimed. Then after a moment her voice became excessively soft. "Why, my dear, how terrible you look! How old and sunken your cheeks are!"

"You've been crying," cried Radames.

"Aren't you well treated here—not like a captured slave but as my personal companion? Speak up, what is it?" Some of the softness was gone from Amneris' voice. She heard Radames breathing heavily.

AIDA THEME

pp

"I am unhappy, your highness, because I heard just now that my country is again at war." Aida spoke rapidly. She tried not to look at Radames.

Amneris frowned. "You followed me here just to tell me that?"

"Oh, I didn't follow you, believe me," cried Aida. "But when I saw you were here, I came over, of course. But if you wish me to leave, your highness—."

"No. I wish you to stay." Amneris' voice was again like honey. She glanced from Aida to Radames. "Aida, have you met our young warrior Radames? But of course you have! He is here so often, aren't you Radames?"

"Yes," said Radames uncomfortably, "I am." He was thinking of something better to say when another round of trumpet calls echoed down the great hall.

"Something's going on in the street. Shall I go look?" he asked with energy.

In disdain the princess waved her fan towards the great steps. "You are much too valuable here with us," she answered smiling. "You must stay and keep Aida and me amused."

"You have but to command," stammered Radames. He saw that Amneris was again glancing at Aida and then at himself—like a tiger, he thought.

We must talk or she will find out our love by our silence! "Your highness, have you seen the high priest Ramphis this morning?" he asked aloud.

"Him! He spends most of his time with my father. They are, in fact, getting ready a public announcement."

"Oh," said Aida.

"Good," cried Radames. "I like public announcements." He turned to Aida. "You haven't seen any in Memphis yet, have you? Well first—after the crowds gather, of course—come the high ranking warriors, then the priests with incense pots. They form a great half-circle facing the people. Then—" but a blast of trumpets filled the hall.

They all turned to look. People were running along the streets toward the palace; people were climbing the stairs to the great hall.

"The whole town is coming here!" exclaimed Aida.

The princess Amneris laughed. "Almost," she said gaily. "Aida, my dear, since this is your first appearance at a public announcement, you should feel as excited as a child."

"I have seen public announcements in my own country," Aida replied with dignity. "I expect they are rather similar to yours."

"Indeed," Amneris moved her fan rapidly. She laughed again. "We shall see. Come, let's all stand over here."

The great hall was filled with the peculiar sound of sandaled feet. More trumpets blared. A group of slaves scurried up the ropes to the reed baskets hung from the ceiling and began to ply the fans. Like great sails of papyrus, the fans flapped to and fro on their creaking mechanisms. The soldiers and the priests filed in and took their places. The black robes of the priests swayed in unison with their incense pots, with the great fans; but their chant was lost in the murmur of the crowd.

"All quiet—the King!"

Radames looked to where the princess Amneris was pointing. He saw the flicker of torches at the royal door set deep in the shadowy side of the hall. A fanfare of trumpets pierced the air, and the King stepped forth followed by the high priest Ramphis and the seven royal torch bearers. The trumpets ceased.

"Where is that little Aida I am so fond of?" whispered Amneris to Radames. "Oh, there she is by that hieroglyph. How thoughtful of her to leave us alone."

Before the King began to speak, he indicated that a messenger be brought in. White with the exhaustion of running, the lad was carried before the King. As the crowd pushed forward to hear, the messenger gasped out his report: "Oh King of Memphis, the city of Thebes is under seige by the Ethiopians, and an army under King Amonasro is marching down the Nile to take Memphis. He is but three days away."

"Amonasro!" The name was whispered back among the crowd until even those Egyptians standing on the stairs heard. "Amonasro!"

Aida heard it by the hieroglyph as her neighbors muttered it among themselves. "My father! Then he is close," she leaned against the stone.

But the whispers now were growing to mutterings and the mutterings to shouts. First those on the fringe of the crowd began to cry, "Kill Amonasro! Kill the invaders!" Then in a moment more the whole hall was screaming, "To war! To war against the Ethiopians!"

The King of Memphis held up his hands for silence. He knew the people were ready for his announcement.

"People of Memphis," he cried, "justly we go to war against the invaders. We will march up the mighty Nile. We will guard our sacred mother stream. We will defend our country. And with the blessings of Isis, speed into

battle by a warrior newly chosen by Isis—the young, the valiant, the un-
defeated, the favorite of the gods—Radames."

As the King finished, Amneris led Radames from the crowd. They
walked into the crescent before the King, before the high priest Ramphis and
all the hall. Radames felt his face flush with excitement. He heard Amneris call
to him as she stepped away, "To war, Radames, and to victory!" He heard
the din of the crowd echoing her call; and above them all he heard the voice
of Aida crying his name.

Again the King held up his hands.

"Radames," he began when the shouting was still. Radames knelt before
him. "Radames, I order you to the temple of Vulcan, god of all weapons,
there to be armed for this holy battle."

Like a spell arose the chant of the priests:

CHANT   Majestically

Then from out the shouting crowd strode Amneris, singing proudly:

RETURN VICTORIOUS (RITORNA VINCITOR)

Ped

In her hands she carried a royal banner, and this she gave to Radames. And as though this act had been an agreed upon signal, the King with his attendants turned towards his rooms, the rows of priests swung into line behind Radames, and in a cloud of purple incense the whole assembly moved out of the great hall.

All but Aida. She stood by the hieroglyph and her eyes were red.

"Kill my father and return the conqueror—that's what she said. Kill my countrymen and return to Memphis the conqueror."

She knelt beside the stone.

"Oh please, may the gods save my father. May they protect him from harm and bring him freedom of our country." She was suddenly quiet. "And Radames? Oh Radames, you must have victory too! My love cannot return to Memphis beaten, lost. But what have I said? My love standing victorious before the Egyptians, standing stained in the blood of my brothers and my father! My love murdering those whom I love so much! I pray—I pray that . . ." and she was silent.

AIDA'S PRAYER FOR FATHER AND LOVER   Agitated

"How easy to be Amneris now," she began again. "The princess of all she can see, while by her very side I must see nothing and keep myself secret. The princess with only one purpose, while I, the princess with two which work at cross-purposes. I curse the day I was captured by the Egyptian raiders. If I had told them then who I was, I would be dead by now. No more agonies . . . But I have only prolonged my death!"

She was sobbing. "I cannot remember more, for now I am confusing my father and my lover. Kind heaven, look upon me! My love is splitting my heart. I pray—I pray to the gods to have pity, pity on me."

AIDA'S PRAYER TO GODS FOR MERCY

ACT I: *Scene 2*

All had been made ready in the Temple of Vulcan. In the golden tripods the incense smoldered. The sacred bowls were filled, and from out their niches the deities looked down upon the priests as they wove about the high altar. Through the heavy curtains beyond came the sounds of the priestesses in prayer.

The curtains were parted. The priests took up the chant and the priestesses danced before the altar. Then the high priest Ramphis lifted from the altar a

THE PRIESTESSES

Ped

veil spun of silver and moved away among the pillars into the dim recesses of the temple. A heavy door creaked. Ramphis returned with Radames over whose head the veil had been placed.

Solemnly Ramphis chanted: "Behold, oh Vulcan, the warrior leader of Memphis, Radames. Veiled in silver, strong of purpose he comes to beg the

anointed sword tempered by the gods—the sword of terror and of death."

From the mouths of the tripods the incense seemed to sink away and then to billow forth again. Ramphis lifted the sword from the altar. He placed it in Radames' right hand.

SONG OF RAMPHIS

intoned the high priest Ramphis.
As his voice sank, Radames and
the priests began to repeat the prayer.

ACT II: *Scene 1*

A score of busy slaves flitted about the princess Amneris as she lay on her couch in the hanging gardens of the palace in Memphis. One slave sprinkled rose-water; one blew dusting powder; two were at work gilding the princess' long fingernails. Shells of rouge and vessels of fragrant oils stood open on a little stand by her side. At last Amneris asked for her mirror. Very carefully she looked at herself in the tiny curl of silver held by the slave at her elbow.

"That will do for the hair, and the eye lashes. Yes, and the lips too," she announced. Then she sighed. "Tell me the time."

"It is past eleven by the sun dial, your highness," whispered the slave with the princess' golden sandals.

"It moves so slowly today. Almost as slowly as you do." Amneris was addressing her slaves in general.

"It is because of the celebration, your highness."

"How clever of you to say so! Yes indeed, I suppose it is because of the celebration. And because of the celebration I must go out, and because of that I must look my best, and because of that Radames will parade at the city walls—all because of a that!" Clearly the princess' patience was wearing thin.

"Oh the brave Radames," breathed the slave with the dusting powder. "To think that he saved our city!"

Amneris sighed again.

"Do I really look well in this cloak?" she asked the slave at her elbow.

"Yes, yes, your highness."

"Yes, green is really your color," echoed the slave who waved the plumed fan.

"Ah," and Amneris sighed yet again.

AMNERIS JEALOUSY THEME   **Agitated**

pp

Ped

AMNERIS JEALOUSY THEME (concluded)

"Thank God," gasped Aida.

"And he's mine," stormed Amneris, fury tugging at her throat. "He loves me, the princess—not you, the slave. Do you hear that! Ho! do you think you would be tolerated here if he loved you?"

Aida had thrown herself at Amneris' feet, but now she arose and drawing herself to her full height, she faced the princess of Memphis. "A woman

of deceit. Oh what is love
to you? How do you
treat it? Did you ever
know what love is? Has Radames.
told you he loves you? Has he?
No, I see it in your face
that he has not. And he
never will. He never will,
princess Amneris."

"You dare to talk to me
like this!"

"I dare a good deal more,
princess Amneris. You think me
a slave, a pawn to be played
with, to act kindly towards
if such is your whim. Yet I tell you

I am—" She stopped. "I am flesh and blood even as you," she added quickly.

"So your game is to provoke me further!" cried Amneris.

A blast of festive music burst beneath the palace wall. Amneris' eyes gleamed even brighter. She pointed towards the city gate. "Did you hear that? The victory celebration has begun! And you, you shall help in a special victory. You will sit in the dust while I sit beside my father the King. I command you, come to the ceremonies. You with your tear stained face can see what your chances are with Radames."

With one sweep of her hand the princess Amneris gathered up her sea-green cloak and stalked towards the porch.

Aida watched her disappear into the coolness of the palace, and not a muscle moved on her face.

Then slowly she murmured, "At least I did not tell her who I am."

With increasing softness, she smiled. It was a tiny smile, a prayer to the gods.

AIDA'S PRAYER TO GODS FOR MERCY

ACT II: *Scene 2*

The noise at the city gate was deafening.
Warriors, dancers, priests, the court and the common
people all trampled the sand before the royal
reviewing stand. Some were shouting, some were
cheering, some threw gaily colored balls hissing into the air.
Most of all the crowd kept chanting in
their high- pitched Egyptian tongue:

GLORY TO EGYPT AND ISIS With great pomp

At one minute past noon the King of Memphis and Amneris the princess attended by their retinue of slaves, began to descend the walled gardens from the palace. When the throng by the gate saw their ruler approaching such a din of welcome arose that the fronds of the date palms quivered. The King was smiling. He continued to smile as he and Amneris took their seats in the stand before the city wall. All the priests moved forward.

"The victory dancers are ready, my lord," whispered the high priest Ramphis, putting his lips to the left ear of the King in order to be heard.

"Let them begin, then," ordered the King.

With some difficulty a space was cleared before the stand and into the area were led twelve young girls dressed all in beads and holding their heads to one side while their hands whirled before them. The King watched their dance with pleasure, but Amneris only glanced at the exotic configuration. Restlessly her eyes moved about on the crowd, as from her commanding position she scrutinized first one face, then another, and still another in the throng before her.

Finally, in the shadow of the wall she caught sight of Aida; and her face relaxed, she sat back in her chair, she turned to laugh with her father.

But in a clash of cymbals the dance had whirled to an end.

From the windows above the gate nine bronze trumpeters blew nine bronze trumpets. And then from the distance beyond the gate sounded the Triumphal March.

Ped

The priests held aloft the carved images of their gods. The Egyptian army swung through the gate and into the city. Following them rolled the chariots of war, crammed with the treasures taken from the defeated. Last of all came Radames, marching under a canopy of billowing purple and yellow carried by his officers. He halted before the royal stand. He began to bow to the King.

"Radames," cried the King, "Savior of Egypt!" and he descended the steps of the stand.

Radames bowed again. This time as he arose he noticed Amneris lifting a wreath of silver from a cushion held by a slave. Now she too descended the steps.

"Hail, Radames," she cried and she placed the wreath upon his head.

"Radames, victor over the invaders, pride of the gods," and the King cleared his throat, "Egypt is most grateful for your valor." Then booming so that all the crowd could hear, the King continued, "Whatever you ask shall be granted, Radames."

"Oh King," replied Radames, surprised by this warmth, "first let us bring in the prisoners."

The King of Memphis reflected a moment, then nodded his head in assent. The crowd pressed forward; and Radames' officers began to lead through the gate a straggling line of men, chained together like cattle, their clothes torn and dirty. The last of these prisoners wore only a lion skin, but he had on his head two curling horns as a helmet.

As he passed Aida, her lips suddenly parted. With a cry she broke through the officers and rushed to the prisoner. But what they said to each other in that first moment was lost in the rattle of chains and the calls of the crowd. Amneris did not notice Aida clinging to the arm of the prisoner, for her eyes were on Radames, and Radames, in the royal presence, was facing the King.

"Well!" The King had spotted Aida. "Look who has joined the captives. Your little friend, my dear. You there in the lion skin, step forward," the King commanded. "What is your name? Who are you? Why does this girl cling to your arm?"

"Great King of
Memphis, I am a warrior.
This girl is my daughter
whom I thought to be
dead. You should know
how she was captured
in a raid by Egyptians.
Many more were taken in
that same raid—and
where are they now?"

The King was annoyed
and in his annoyance
he forgot his unanswered
question. Before the
surprised Radames could
speak, he waved his hands

towards the huddle of prisoners. "And here *you* are, now!" he cried in irony.

"Don't interrupt him," hastily whispered Amneris to Radames. Then she added beaming, "You've done well to bring her father into our power!"

"You look more intelligent than most," continued the King scornfully, still addressing the prisoner. "Tell me, do you acknowledge that you are beaten, do you recognize that you are prisoners of Egypt?"

In the silence that followed the prisoner looked at his countrymen crouched about him. Then he swung his head again towards the King. Softly yet proudly he began to speak and with each word his voice grew stronger:

AMONASRO'S PLEA   With vigor

"Mighty King, great in your splendor of victory. You see here only the last few survivors of an army. Know you that the King of the Ethiopians fell in the dust at my feet and that the cream of the army of the Ethiopians were slaughtered. In vain we too sought our death on the field. Yet instead we were chained and dragged to you. Victorious King, remember that we too fought for our country. If that is a crime, we too are guilty."

The crowd remained hushed. Everyone in the throng by the city walls stood watching the prisoner in the helmet and Aida white on his arm.

"Tomorrow, mighty King, think of tomorrow!" the prisoner continued. "Who knows how all your battles may go? Look upon us and see here the misery of defeat. May you never have to suffer this which we now suffer. And let you remember that mercy is a quality victory can most afford."

He ceased. Around him his countrymen murmured, "Pity, oh King, pity."

With a sob in her voice, Aida called up to the royal stand, "Mercy on us all, oh King."

Radames and the court and the priests and the crowd looked at Aida and her countrymen. A murmur of sympathy began to run among the throng. Aida, who had bowed her head after her appeal, now raised her face to the King. Her eyes met Radames. The King was pursing his lips, his head slowly nodding. Aida stepped back to her father; but still Radames' eyes followed her. A ripple of a smile was replacing his anxiety. It ran around his mouth and his eyes. Amneris, by his side, stiffened.

Then Radames turned again to the King. "Oh most gracious King," he began, "I have a wish. My wish is that the Ethiopians be freed."

"Impossible!" cried the high priest Ramphis before the King could speak.

He raised both hands. "Impossible," he cried again.

"Impossible," echoed the long line of priests, each shaking his shaven head and holding up his protesting hands.

"Ignore their tricks and their voices, oh King. The gods have granted us this victory," thundered Ramphis, turning from the King to the crowd and then back to the King. "We must not dishonor our gods at this hour. Think of Egypt!"

"The gods have favored us, that is true," responded the King.

"And you, young hero," cried Ramphis turning to Radames, "listen to the advice of wiser men. Let not triumph turn your head to silly wishes. These prisoners of the gods must be offered up as fitness decides. How can they possibly go free?"

Cries of disagreement arose from the crowd. In the turmoil Radames' astonished voice reached the King: "Oh King, you have given your promise even as I have given my wish!"

The King remained silent and gradually the shouting died. The priests and the throng by the gate became still; and all eyes turned on the King.

"Events have smiled upon us," the King began slowly. "We are a grateful people and our gods are grateful gods. Pity is known to please heaven—and to confirm the power of Kings." He paused. The high priest Ramphis was slipping towards him.

"Oh King," he said quickly in a low voice, "I will agree that all prisoners but Aida and her father be freed. I propose we hold those two as hostages against further attacks."

The King seemed pleased. Again he cleared his throat; he raised his hand. It was the sign of a proclamation. The slaves held their great fans motionless.

"All are to go free except Aida and her father. So be it!" the King proclaimed three times. The trumpets blew.

Then the King held up his hand again.

"My daughter, Amneris, and Radames, my warrior—stand here!" Both Amneris and Radames moved to the edge of the stand before the King.

"Radames," the King cried, "as reward I give you the hand of Amneris. In two waxings of the moon you shall be married, and when I am gone you shall be King and rule after me."

Radames was too astonished to speak, but his eyes sought out Aida on the sand before the gate, while around him burst choruses of praise and behind him the joyous Amneris embraced her father.

ACT III

Moonlight painted the sand in scattered patches under the sighing palm trees lining the bank of the Nile. Rising out of heavy shadow, the stones of the Temple of Isis sloped towards the sky, reddened now by a glow from the city of Memphis on the far shore. For in Memphis all the bronze lamps were lit; torches flamed from every street corner; the great palace gleamed in illumination—all by order of the King for this last evening before the royal wedding of Amneris and Radames.

The rustling and sighing wind from the water blew with it a chant of priests and priestesses, wafted from inside the Temple. Then the wind, blending all with the whispers of the night-blooming flowers, faded into the dense groves behind the shore. Suddenly into these sounds came the splash of oars; then the murmur of voices. A barge was being moored on the bank before the Temple of Isis.

"Oh Amneris," came the voice of the high priest Ramphis, "see that your veil is lowered and that of your servants as well."

"It is. We are ready and waiting," Amneris sounded exultant. "Nothing will spoil the marriage prayers to Isis, rest assured of that."

"It is in the hands of Isis," replied the high priest as the dim mass of figures mounted the steps to the Temple. In a moment they disappeared inside.

Then noiselessly a shadow detached itself from the darkness of the Temple wall, a single figure moved forward on the sand. Between the patches of moonlight Aida made her way to the water's edge.

"She is so happy. So very happy. And now the gods will insure that happiness. Against Egypt what can *I* do? Against Egypt what has dear Radames been able to do? Or my father?"

Aida stopped by the last palm tree. She looked long at the ripples on the

Nile. "If he meets me here just to say goodbye," she whispered, "I will kill myself. I will walk into the Nile and sleep on its deep bed—forever. There as near to Radames as I can ever be." Her voice broke into sobs.

Then after a minute she went on in a firmer tone. "Here under these little waves—how far from home! My home of bright-blue skies, of warmth, of childhood, my happy days gone by!"

AIDA'S SONG OF HOME (O PATRIA MIA)

"Aida! Aida!"
Aida whirled and peered into the shadows.
"Father, why did you come here?" she demanded. "Have you news? Have you another plan?"
"I have both."
"Both, father?"

"Yes. The news has been a long time in reaching me; but it came this afternoon. Until it came—how could I raise more false hopes!" Amonasro put his hand on his daughter's shoulder. "Aida," he continued, "just now I heard you singing of our dear country. And you still in love with an Egyptian—and also in love with Ethiopia! Radames is—."

"Radames you are not to talk about," broke in Aida. "Hasn't he helped us all he could? Hasn't he gotten us the liberty of the city? Hasn't he even tried to—."

"He has done all these things, that is very true," said her father. "He has done them for you."

"Well."

"Now soon we will have more than the mere freedom of Memphis, Aida. We will have the freedom of Ethiopia again."

"Father! How?"

"You will see our land again, live like a princess again in our own palace. Your laughter will ring among our hills and through our valleys. Home! Think of it, Aida!" Amonasro tugged at his daughter's shoulder.

"Yes, father, I have scarcely ever stopped thinking of it. Even when," and Aida paused, "even when I thought of Radames." She patted her father's hand.

"There you will be King again, father."

"Aida, it is great news I've brought. Come, stop being so— so— oh, I don't know."

"You are free, father, to escape whenever you can. But I, I am a prisoner here, chained by invisible links. Here I must stay to be near Radames. There is no such thing as escape for me. You must understand there is no escape."

"Aida, my child, there *is* escape." Her father tugged again at her shoulder. "Listen to me. You can come home with me. You can have your revenge on this princess, this vile Egyptian woman who has Radames in her power. You hate her no more than I. And you can marry Radames. I have no quarrel with him. If you had not spent so much of your time by yourself you would know more of my plans. You would know that your happiness is my concern. And you would know that your happiness is possible."

"With Radames in Ethiopia? How?"

"Yes, with Radames and in Ethiopia. In fact, Radames will help us." Amonasro was all briskness now, yet he watched Aida's face closely in the moonlight as he continued, "Listen carefully. We have regrouped our army secretly on the frontier. Smaller than before, to be sure, but still larger than anyone here can imagine. If we can surprise the Egyptians this time, we will win."

Aida nodded her head.

"We must not fail, Aida," Amonasro continued, "and you have done well thus far. You have spread my stories of our utter defeat, and you are believed. They think that no army exists."

Aida shuddered a little. Amonasro gripped her shoulder.

"You know—and I know—an invasion of Ethiopia will begin in a few days. A kind of celebration of this wedding, as it were. Obviously by now the route these Egyptians will use has been decided upon. But what is that route? Ha! that's a secret neither of us can discover."

Again Aida nodded.

"But it can be discovered. You can find out from Radames. Tonight."

"No!" cried Aida. She shrank from her father; she turned into the shadow. "How can you ask such a thing? How can you dare think I would betray Radames?"

"Betray? Betray?" Amonasro was again at Aida's side. "Who is doing the betraying? You are betraying your country—or don't you know that? This is more than your happiness. Doesn't it matter to you whether the Egyptians burn our villages? They will throw flaming torches into the doors of all the houses and let the people inside burn to death. They will listen

gladly to the screams; and when they become tired of this, they will move on to another village. At night they will drop poison into the wells there, so that next day one after another the people will take sick and die in the streets. Is it mercy you ask? Is it pity?"

Amonasro grasped Aida by the arms. "You are no daughter of mine! You are an Egyptian slave!"

He threw her to the ground.

Aida lay motionless on the cool sand. She heard the lapping of the Nile where it wriggled like a snake at the shore. She heard another chant begin in the Temple. Then she spoke: "I will do what I can, father."

Amonasro bent down. He helped her to her feet.

AMONASRO'S SONG TO AIDA   **Broadly**

"Aida," he said, "you are my daughter!" And he held her in his arms. "Think," he told her when her face was dry, "how all Ethiopia will rejoice at what you have done!"

Aida smiled a little. "Think too," she said in a voice so low it was like the lapping of the water, "how much my love is costing me."

But her father only patted her arm again. Already he was looking up the dark river towards Ethiopia and his brows contracted. He seemed to be deep in his plans. Once or twice he shook his head. Suddenly, however, he turned to Aida. "When do you meet him?" he asked.

"Radames?"

"Yes. See over there," and Amonasro pointed to a darker patch on the Nile. "Someone is coming in a boat."

"It must be Radames for he's never late. But I am so early it always makes him seem so late."

"Good," replied Amonasro, uneasy with excitement. "Remember I leave our country's fate in your hands, my daughter. And if you should need me," he continued as he drew back towards the Temple wall, "remember I'll be here."

Aida put her hands to her face. She ran her fingers over her cheeks and into her hair. She smoothed her dress. Then she walked slowly to the edge of the shore where the ripples wasted on the sand. The dark patch had moved in on her right and was blending with the darker shore. There was a faint splash. Then silence. Then, "My love!" and Radames was by her side, had taken her in his arms.

After a time Aida tried to draw her lips away. "Haven't you mistaken me for the princess Amneris?" she murmured. "Such love you should save for her."

"Aida, hush!"

"But how should I act? Do you truly love me, Radames?"

"Truly, Aida. You and only you."

"But what hope is there for us—for our love?"

"All hope, my darling—"

"Yet this is our last night, Radames," cried Aida. "Oh, how short is happiness!"

"I will not marry Amneris." Radames was growing stubborn.

"Radames, you can't! In the face of the King, of the priests, of the people—you *dare* go against Egypt! You will be killed. My darling, you don't know what you are saying."

"But just let me finish!" exclaimed Radames, "and stop having me disposed of so quickly. You don't know yet, probably, but we in the army have had news that bands of Ethiopians are burning the towns on our border. The stories are pretty gruesome—and you know what that means."

Aida shook he head. "No," she sighed, "you will be married to Amneris by this time tomorrow."

"I will—and I won't. I'll leave early tomorrow before the wedding ceremonies to lead our army into Ethiopia—for how else should a commander
act? And when I return victorious I'll ask the King to let me marry you.
I'll open my heart to the King and you will be the reward of my new
glory. Why, how could he refuse!"

"My darling," Aida's voice was firm, "did the King keep his word after
your first victorious return? No. Will Amneris relinquish you so easily?
No. Will my life or my father's be safe from her revenge should she suspect
you wanted to marry me? No, no, I tell you, Radames, your plan will not
work. You were promised before all of Memphis, before the priests, before
Amneris herself, by the King himself. Think! What good have all your
plans come to for me, or my father? Are we even allowed to leave Memphis?
And the priests, they would certainly forbid any marriage with a foreigner.
And, and suppose you never returned?"

Aida did not quite stifle a sob.

"Well, but—" began Radames.

"Do you really love me, truly?" asked Aida for the second time.

"Yes, truly. You know I do."

"Then there is a way out."

"What?"

"Radames, we can go away together to another country—go tonight. To a country where the age-old forests send shade to cool grass and to charm the flowers; where the air is not so hot as here. A beautiful country. And you will love it as you love me. No waste of sand, there, no desert just beyond the city walls but a fresh land of meadows and pools, a quiet joy, a world where love is everywhere. Oh Radames, come!"

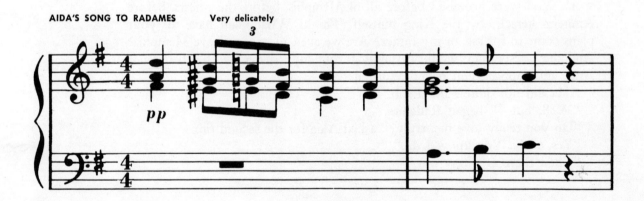

AIDA'S SONG TO RADAMES   Very delicately

Tenderly Radames ruffled her hair.

"Aida," he said slowly, "and where can such a country be? Do you want to know what I think of your scheme? It won't work either. How could I possibly leave Egypt?"

"Yes, you can. But it must be now—before tomorrow. Before you are tied by the duties of commander and husband. Tonight you are still free. We can slip away now and be far from Memphis before you are missed."

"Aida, you don't understand. How could I leave my country? Why must you have me desert Egypt? This is the land I have always known. Here I grew up. Here I have fought, and here they now pay me honor."

"I pay you love."

"But, Aida, there's glory here!"

"Do you want glory or do you want love? We cannot be alive and love in Egypt, Radames. And as for honor and glory, why can't you earn both again in our new home? It will not be hard."

"Well," replied Radames at last, "in time, perhaps. But think of what we'd leave behind. These stars, Aida," and he swept his hand across the sky, "these stars in this sky were the ones that looked first on our love. We would abandon even them!"

"There are more, many more in other skies, Radames."

"But we must remain here. It is better, Aida."

"Why? It is better only if you want to marry Amneris."

"I will not marry Amneris, I tell you."

"And yet you will not come?" Her question wavered on her lips. "You will not come?"

"No, Aida, it is—"

"It is that I mean nothing to you, then!" exclaimed Aida. Hot tears fell on Radames' arm as she shook herself free.

"Now I see you have been making fun of me, playing with me and saying you loved me. Go get into your boat! Go back to Memphis, mighty Memphis. Marry the powerful Amneris. And forget all about me."

"Aida!"

"Forget how you kissed a poor captive girl. Forget your kindness to her father. Forget me. I do not exist any longer."

She had started to run.

In a bound Radames was at her side.

"Aida, listen to me! How can I tell you how I love you? You must listen. That's better . . . Now—"

"Will you come with me?"

"Now come and sit down so we can talk."

"Will you come with me?"

Radames was silent.

"Will you come?" Aida persisted.

"Let's sit over there by the Temple wall. It's so very dark there it's easier to talk."

"I have nothing to talk about," replied Aida, "and you are to forget me."

"It's too far a journey to risk," Radames said finally. They had seated themselves against the Temple wall. "The risk is too great, Aida," repeated Radames when Aida made no reply.

"It's risking no more to stay here—unless you want Amneris."

"I do *not* want Amneris! How many times—"

"Then will you come with me tonight?" Aida repeated before he had finished.

"Why must we settle that now? I've told you that I won't be married to her and . . . and . . . ," his voice trailed into silence.

Aida rose.
"Aida, it
would take days
just to get out
of Egypt!"
Radames was
begging.
"What are
days, Radames,
when we will
then have
years?"
"Yes, I
know." Radames
was silent.
Then he too stood
up. "We could
hide all right, I suppose.

I know the country well, you know. And if we traveled only at night until we crossed the border . . ." He spoke in a halting voice.

"Of course, darling." Aida put her head against Radames. "You will come then, tonight?"

There was a long silence. The wind blew of only the liquids of the Nile; the muffled chanting from inside the Temple had ceased.

Finally Radames whispered, "Yes."

"Darling!" murmured Aida.

For some time they remained silent, deep within the darkness of the Temple wall. Then suddenly Aida said, "We must start; it's very late. It will soon be morning."

"Ah my dearest, don't worry so," Radames laughed. "We'll get a little ways tonight. I know how to avoid the traffic on the Great Road."

"But how can we avoid the Egyptian Army?" asked Aida.

"That's easy. You just let me worry about them. We'll skirt them—they're all grouped in the Gorge of Napata."

"Excellent!"

"Who's that?"

"Excellent!" and Amonasro leaped from the darkness. He caught hold of

Aida and Radames. "The Egyptians are defeated! My army will bottle up the gorge."

"Father, how you frightened us!"

"Your army?"

"*My* army."

"Father—"

"I am Amonasro, King of the Ethiopians. The King, Radames—"

"Father, what are you saying!" Aida was trembling so much she could scarcely speak.

"Of the Ethiopians." Radames voice was thick. He seemed to grow rigid. Then suddenly his shoulders slumped and he leaned heavily on Aida and Amonasro.

"Well, well. It is a shock, to be sure," said Amonasro, "but I promise that success and happiness await you in my kingdom, Radames. I am a man of my word. You and Aida already have my blessing."

Radames moaned.

Aida knelt on the sand before him. "Darling," she cried, "it is all for the best. Believe me."

Radames struggled free of Amonasro.

"I have betrayed Egypt! Do you hear? I have betrayed Egypt!" Radames was shouting.

"Hush, darling, hush. Someone will hear!"

"Come," cried Amonasro, "it is too late to repent." He still gripped Radames. "And you have no need to shout like this. You are not guilty. Fate has already betrayed you, not you your honor. Come," and he released Radames, "stand on your new duty—make good your escape with us now."

"Come," began Aida.

There was a scrape of stone on the Temple stairs.

"Seize them!" screamed the voice of Amneris from out of the darkness. There are plotters here!"

In a moment torches were swarming about the Temple door and dancing down the upper steps.

"Treacherous prisoners, I heard you," Amneris shrieked. She pointed a long white finger towards Aida and Amonasro. "Of you two, all I need say: you have proved your trickery—and you shall die for it. But you, you, Radames! Treachery beyond treachery! Betrayer of your country, your gods, yourself! What can happen now to you?"

Amonasro drew his dagger and strode towards the Temple steps.

"Stop! Are you mad!" shouted Radames when he saw where the Ethiopian was going. "Go—escape now. There is time."

In surprise Amneris and her guards paused. Then the high priest Ramphis shrilled, "Seize them! Seize them all!" and the Egyptians swept down the last flight.

Radames stood motionless. The Egyptian guards swirled past him. Only one paused at his side and he too rushed on into the dense gardens as soon as Amneris and Ramphis reached the prisoner. Slowly Radames bowed his head. And his red cloak fell in a pool of silk at his feet. Under the flaring torch of the high priest, he bowed in disgrace and despair.

Very quietly he said, "I have no more to do. I give you my sword."

He unbuckled his sword, and turning the blade towards himself he handed the hilt to Ramphis.

Eastward over the gardens where the shouting was fading a touch of morning light flushed the sky.

ACT IV: *Scene 1*

"Bring the prisoner to me, at once!" Amneris' voice rang harshly along the bleak corridor, but her hands clutched one another under her cape and she leaned against the wall for support. Then her voice returned: "At once, do you hear!"

One of the company of guards bowed and disappeared through the low doorway at the far end of the corridor. His footsteps clattered on the stone of some hidden stair; then abruptly they ceased.

ACT IV

Scene 1

Amneris continued to lean against the wall of the bare corridor which connected the dungeons with the Judgment Hall. Then she heard the footsteps of two persons climbing the hidden stairs. The black veil covering her head fluttered; she raised her right hand. "Go—leave us," she commanded. Obedient to the royal order, the remaining guards separated and moved to the doors leading from the corridor. Every door held two guards, but the corridor itself was empty. Through the low doorway stepped the returning guard and Radames.

"You, too, leave us," ordered the princess to the last guard.

"We are alone for only a moment," murmured Amneris as she approached Radames. "Look at me, Radames! For only a moment, Radames. Already the priests are assembled in the inner chambers of the Judgment Hall. They will find you guilty! I know they will. You must defend yourself. Explain how the secret was wrung from you. Talk to them. And meanwhile I will run to my father and beg him to send a pardon. Quickly, Radames—"

"I have nothing to explain to either gods or men," Radames said slowly.

"Think!"

Radames squared his shoulders. His eyes still pierced the air above Amneris' head. "My reasons and my honor remain pure. My tongue was incautious— that is all."

"Then say so—tell the priests so and you will live. I swear, you will live."

"Live! For what?"

"For my love. Is it so poor a thing? For the country, then—for the kingdom. For life, Radames—breath! How can you die! I have undergone the anguishes of death for you already. I walked through these long nights watching the stars for you. I have offered everything for you." Amneris tried to steady herself.

"For her I gave the country, the kingdom. For her—"

"I will not hear of *her!*" The princess' hand jerked beneath her cape.

"Infamy is my fate—and you want me to live!" Radames' lips curled slightly. "How utterly wretched do you think you can make me? You have killed Aida."

"I have not killed Aida."

Radames looked at Amneris. "No?" he asked, a rush of color on his face.

"No. She has disappeared. But her father was caught and killed in the gardens."

"Ah," Radames' eyes returned to the air above the head of the princess Amneris. "Then may she by now have returned safe to her happy childhood home and never know more of Radames who will die for her sake."

"Oh, enough of Aida," broke in Amneris wildly. "I can't bear her name. Radames, you must swear that if I save you you will never mention her again."

"No."

"Swear! Swear!"

"No."

"Renounce her, Radames. I will save you."

"I am ready to die."

Amneris flung her cape from her shoulders. Her fists beat the air before Radames. "Are you mad? Oh, revenge, my revenge, what form does it now take?" Blindly she turned and stumbled against the corridor wall. "Instead of love, a fury; and in place of life, death."

She sank to the floor. "Gods in heaven, make my revenge ready."

The guards sprang from their doorways. One group rushed to the side of the princess, while the rest grasped Radames and led him back through the low door. The clank of their steps on the secret stairs resounded in the corridor.

"Help her up, the priests are coming." The guards were lifting Amneris to her feet.

"Let me alone. Let me die, for who can save him? And I, I was the one

ACT IV
Scene 1

who threw him to the priests. I have caused his death, do you hear?"

"Shh-hh, your highness; here come the priests!"

"Yes, here they are. Those fatal, merciless ministers," and Amneris buried her face in her hands.

The guards stood at attention for the priests to file past.

THEME OF THE PRIESTS   Solemnly

Suddenly through her hands Amneris screamed: "He is innocent—do you hear—innocent!"

Her voice was lost in the chant of Ramphis the high priest. The guards hurried to close the doors to the Judgment Hall.

"No, no. I must hear, please," Amneris was sobbing. She began to creep

along the wall towards the great doors, but the guards paid no attention to her. One half the door was swung to.

"Stop! Do you hear me! I command you—leave the door. Go!" With some of the fierceness of her former self Amneris clutched at the guards nearest to her.

For a moment the company of guards exchanged glances; then one of them shrugged his shoulders. They left the great door half closed and moved away together towards the dungeons. Amneris pressed her body in the wedge

of the door. She could see a slice of the Hall where, against the black ramp, the high priest stood all in white. He had finished leading the priests in their customary prayer to the gods for justice, and now he was addressing Radames.

"Radames, Radames, hear now the counts against you. One: you have revealed Egypt's most guarded secrets to a foreigner. What do you say?"

"Defend yourself, Radames," chanted the priests.

There was silence.

"He is silent," said Ramphis to the priests.

"Then he is guilty," cried the priests.

Ramphis nodded. "Radames, Radames," he continued. "Two: you deserted your camp in the city of Memphis the evening before you were to lead the army into Ethiopia."

"Defend yourself," warned the priests, "defend yourself, Radames."

There was silence.

"He is silent," said Ramphis to the priests.

"Guilty then," cried the priests.

Ramphis nodded. "Radames, Radames. Three: you have broken your allegiance to Egypt, to her King, and to your own honor."

"Defend yourself, Radames."
There was silence.
"He is silent still," said Ramphis.
"Guilty then," cried
the priests. "Guilty on all counts."
"Oh gods, save my Radames!
Speak to your servants, the priests,"
Amneris' dry lips could
scarcely form her prayer.
Ramphis was raising his hands, a white
colossus against the black ramps.
"The judgment, Radames, Radames.
Your fate is to die beneath the altar
of the god you have so angered—the god Vulcan.
We condemn you to be buried alive in the
tomb beneath the altar of the god Vulcan."

"To suffocate! My Radames!" Amneris tried to push her arms into the Hall, but the great doors did not move. She sank to the threshold. "Oh gods, to such a fate! And they who condemn him call themselves ministers of heaven!"

Amneris the princess ceased to move.

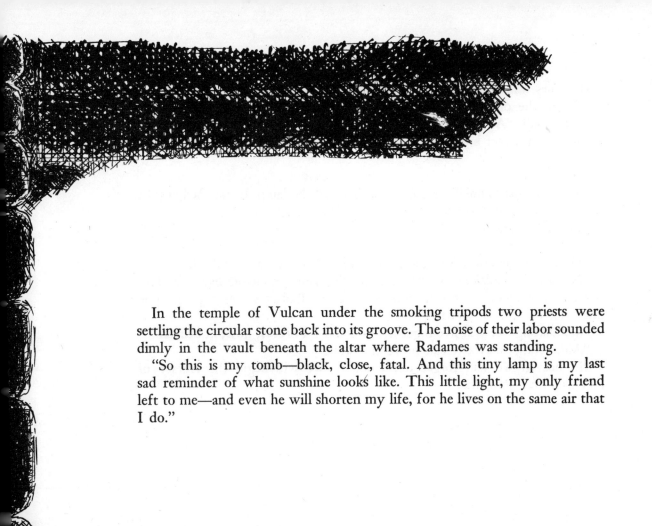

In the temple of Vulcan under the smoking tripods two priests were settling the circular stone back into its groove. The noise of their labor sounded dimly in the vault beneath the altar where Radames was standing.

"So this is my tomb—black, close, fatal. And this tiny lamp is my last sad reminder of what sunshine looks like. This little light, my only friend left to me—and even he will shorten my life, for he lives on the same air that I do."

Radames walked slowly away from the staircase.

"Is this the direction towards Ethiopia and Aida, I wonder?" he asked himself aloud. "At least I can go towards her as far as the rock will let me. Happy Aida, never knowing of my fate, living her life in the—what's that? A ghost!"

"It is I."

"You—in this tomb?" Radames had dropped the lamp. In the darkness he stumbled forward. "Where? Aida, where are you?"

"Here, Radames."

He found her.

"Here in your arms, Radames. Here I have always wished to die."

"Not to die, Aida! So beautiful, so lovely, you cannot die like this. This is meant for criminals, for traitors. Aida," and Radames was crying, "you must not die. I love you too much."

"My darling, we will live together, you and I. Forever, now, in heaven."

"Aida, come, maybe I can move the stone."

"In heaven we will forget our troubles; we will begin the ecstasy of immortal love, Radames."

"Come quickly, we have no time to lose," and holding Aida with one hand Radames began groping about with the other.

SONG OF RAMPHIS

"That chant! It leads this way, and—here is the staircase, Aida. Now," and Radames ran his hands along the ceiling, "here." And he pushed with all his strength.

"It doesn't move! Aida, it doesn't move!"

He tried again, and then again.

"I can't do anything, Aida. You are doomed!" and crying in despair Radames stumbled from the staircase.

Gently Aida took his hands. Very gently she sat him down on the cold stone of the floor. She put her head in his lap. They were very quiet.

"That song, how sad it is," she murmured at length.

"Ah, yes, that song. I remember when I first heard it, Aida. The priests sang it when I was made commander beside that very altar." Radames took a deep breath. He was almost panting. "And I thought it was very proud and rousing then."

"It is a hymn of death, my Radames," replied Aida slowly. "We must sing our own song instead of listening to this one." She too was breathing hard. "Our farewell to the earth—to our dream of joy, now vanishing, and to the heaven opening to our wandering souls."

AIDA'S FAREWELL TO EARTH

Ped

Scene 2   Aida's and Radames' voices faded in the impenetrable depth of the tomb.
And at that very moment in the temple above, the haggard princess Amneris
slipped between the horrified priests and flung herself on the sealed stone.
"My love, I pray for you, Radames," she whispered.

MEET THE COMPOSER

Giuseppe Fortunino Francesco Verdi was born early in the nineteenth century (October 10, 1813, to be exact) in the hamlet of Le Roncole in what was then a part of France, but what is now a part of northern Italy. His parents were very poor and kept a small inn where they sold coffee, sugar, and tobacco. A wandering violinist used to drop into the inn every few weeks to play for the guests and to pass the hat. Whenever he appeared,

Verdi would stop helping his father and stand perfectly still, listening to the violin.

The boy's love of music soon became known throughout the countryside, and when his father decided to allow him to take lessons, a neighbor repaired an old spinet for him for nothing. This battered old spinet Verdi kept all his life. The village organist taught him for a time, and so rapid was his progress that when the organist retired three years later young Verdi became organist in his place.

Verdi's musical education really began at 12, when he left the hamlet of Le Roncole and entered the house of Antonio Barezzi, a wealthy merchant who lived in the nearby town of Busseto. Mr. Barezzi was a trained musician. He soon took a liking to the awkward, earnest Verdi and gave him much encouragement. Under his care Verdi began to compose, writing an overture and marches for the local band. He wrote piano pieces, too, and these he began to play as duets with Mr. Barezzi's pretty daughter. Busseto was a musical town; it had a Philharmonic Society whose orchestra Verdi also began to conduct. When he was 15, he wrote his first symphonic music, and the Philharmonic Society orchestra played it.

For so promising and ambitious a musician and composer, Busseto, in turn, became too small. With the financial aid of Mr. Barezzi and others, Verdi went to the city of Milan in 1832 to study music. Although he was older than the regulations permitted for students to enter the Milan Conservatorio, Verdi applied for admission anyway. He took an examination—and was rejected. He did not give up. He stayed in the city, studying privately, and by his ability and performance he began to attract the attention of important people. He had not forgotten Mr. Barezzi's daughter either. On the fourth of May in 1836 he married her, and they settled in a tiny apartment in Milan.

It was a busy time. Three years later his first opera was produced, "Oberto, Conte di San Bonifacio." The future seemed to lead on to greater happiness. And then within a year Verdi's little boy became ill and died; two days later his little girl died; and then his wife died. Verdi was left alone.

But Verdi had to have money in order to eat and that meant finishing the new opera on which he had been working—a heartbreaking task, for it was, of all things, a comic opera! And it was a failure. Bitterly discouraged by so many misfortunes, Verdi vowed never to write again for the theater.

However, Verdi was a musician who could not stay away from opera, the theater of music. A year later when the impresario of the La Scala Opera asked him to compose another opera, he reluctantly agreed. This one was "Nebuchadnezzar," and it was Verdi's first hit. Almost overnight he leaped from an obscure musician to one of the greatest of the living Italian composers.

"Aida" is one of Verdi's greatest operas. Before he composed it in 1870, he had written other famous operas, including "Rigoletto" in 1851, "Il Trovatore" in 1853, and "La Traviata" in 1853, together with a whole group of now almost forgotten operas.

"Aida" was composed to celebrate two events—the opening of the Suez Canal in Egypt and, incidentally, a new theater in Cairo. None other than the Khedive of Egypt invited Verdi to compose the opera, but Verdi refused. A few months later the invitation was repeated with a large sum of money. Verdi still refused. Finally the plot of the opera was sent to him. He only glanced at it at first, but soon his enthusiasm was aroused. He read it carefully, and the story caught his theatrical instinct—here was a plot which could be told dramatically, beautifully in music. He agreed to write "Aida."

January 1871 had been specified as the month in which "Aida" should have its world premiere in Cairo. Verdi was ready, but the costumes and the scenery were not. They were being made in Paris, the center of the arts of costume and design, but before they were completed Paris had been surrounded and cut off from the rest of the world by the Franco-Prussian War. Mail could be sent from Paris by balloons that drifted far enough to fall into friendly hands; but trunks of costumes and wagon loads of scenery could not yet be carried through the air. "Aida" was postponed. Paris actually fell in January 1871, but by that time it was too late to prepare "Aida" for the opera season in Cairo. Thus it was that almost a year later on Christmas eve "Aida" finally did open in Cairo. It was a triumphant success. It still belongs to the handful of world-famous and constantly-performed operas.

Verdi wrote only two operas after "Aida." Years later following his famous Requiem, he wrote "Otello." He was then nearly 70 years old. When he was 80, his last opera, "Falstaff," was produced in Milan. "Falstaff" and "Otello" both have great dramatic power but the voices and the orchestra are given greater freedom than in "Aida." There are no set arias in "Falstaff." A little over a year after the beginning of our twentieth century, Verdi died in Milan at 10 minutes to three in the morning.